Biogr   5:
The l
resea

Edited by Joanna Bornat

NUMBER 1 IN

THE REPRESENTATION OF OLDER PEOPLE
IN AGEING RESEARCH SERIES

THE CENTRE FOR POLICY ON AGEING AND
THE CENTRE FOR AGEING AND BIOGRAPHICAL
STUDIES AT THE OPEN UNIVERSITY

SERIES EDITORS
SHEILA PEACE AND JOANNA BORNAT

The Open
University

First published in 1999
by the Centre for Policy on Ageing
19-23 Ironmonger Row
London EC1V 3QP
Tel: +44 020 7253 1787
Fax: +44 020 7490 4206
Email: cpa@cpa.org.uk
www.cpa.org.uk

British Library Cataloguing in Publication Data
A catalogue record for this book is available from the British Library

ISBN 1 90109720 X

The Representation of Older People in Ageing Research Series is based on seminars organised by the Centre for Ageing and Biographical Studies, School of Health and Social Welfare, The Open University and the Centre for Policy on Ageing. The first seminar was held in London on 21 June 1996.

Also available in the series:

To obtain a CPA publications catalogue contact: Publications Officer, Centre for Policy on Ageing, 19-23 Ironmonger Row, London EC1V 3QP. Tel: +44 020 7253 1787. CPA publications are distributed by Central Books, 99 Wallis Road, London E9 5LN. Tel: +44 020 8986 5488

Printed by Instant Print, London
Cover design by Sara Chapman

CONTENTS

1

INTRODUCTION
JOANNA BORNAT

'Biographical Interviews: the link between research and practice' was the first seminar in a planned series on 'The Representation of Older People in Ageing Research' run jointly by the Open University and the Centre for Policy on Ageing (CPA). The choice of biography as the starting point for the series was appropriate for both organisations. Members of the School of Health and Social Welfare at the Open University have a long-standing and indeed pioneering interest in the use of biographical methods in health and social care work with older people (Johnson 1976; Bornat 1989). CPA has shown a consistent interest in approaches to care and support which take a 'whole person' focus, where 'whole person' is taken to mean the individual in the context not only of their current social or medical situation but also their past life experiences – their biography.

Biographical, life history and reminiscence based approaches to health and social care work with older people have proved extremely popular over the last fifteen years and more in the UK. Building on ideas set out by Butler (1963), carers have been keen to develop activities and interventions which encourage older people to recall and reflect on their past lives. Researchers, principally in the USA (Haight and Webster 1995) but also in the UK (Coleman 1986; Gibson 1993), have demonstrated positive outcomes when older people are provided with opportunities to recall and review a past life. The enthusiasm of carers and workers, and outputs from researchers, have done much to popularise reminiscence and biographical based approaches in care settings. However, what has been lacking up to now is any extensive advancement of the research and development of good practice in relation to biographical approaches to decision-making and care provision for older people.

There have been some attempts to make links between research and practice using a biographical focus, some of which have been developed by members of the School of Health and Social Welfare. During the late 1980s, in collaboration with the Gloucester Health Authority, a research project,'Care for Elderly People at Home' was funded by Gloucester Health Authority and the Nuffield Provincial Hospitals Fund. This project sought to develop a method whereby older people at risk of no longer being able to cope on their own might have their needs assessed in a context of their past experience. Several reports were published detailing the outputs from this research, as well as a book outlining the biographical interview methods adopted by the care coordinators employed by the project (Boulton *et al.* 1989; Dant and Gully 1994).

Other research funded by the School of Health and Social Welfare and in collaboration with Sir Gordon Roberts College of Nursing and Midwifery also focused on links between theory and practice in biographical work, and included a project aimed at understanding the ways in which nursing staff use biography in communicating with frail elderly people. Carried out on continuing care wards in hospitals in Kettering and Wellingborough this was, in part, action research and resulted in recommendations relating to the adoption of biographical methods in care planning (Adams *et al.* 1996). More recently, an Economic and Social Research Council (ESRC) funded project focusing on the impact of family change on the lives of older people, has used a life history approach to interviewing. Members of the research team, located at the School of Health and Social Welfare, have found that by using a life history, or biographical approach, participants were able to reflect on their lives during the interview and to develop their own understanding, and even language, to describe experiences of family breakdown and reconstitution (Bornat *et al.* 1998).

Examples linking theory and practice are, however, rare and it was with this in mind that the three contributors to the seminar were invited to speak. Each has developed biographical approaches to research and practice in original and creative ways. Our aim was to provoke a discussion focusing on issues raised in their papers and to develop an awareness of the direct contribution which familiarity with a life history can make to good quality care practice. Briefly, our aim was to explore to what extent it is possible to operationalise the stories and narratives which are produced through reminiscence and biographical work. The three speakers came from quite different backgrounds and draw on work with children and with younger disabled people as well as with older people. The opportunities for comparisons and for inferences to be drawn across customary barriers and divisions proved challenging and stimulating.

Dr Prue Chamberlayne is a senior lecturer at the Centre for Biography in Social Policy, University of East London. In her paper she outlines a method of life history interviewing which, she suggests, can empower carers and disabled people with its emphasis on the interpretation of meanings and dynamics in relationships developed over a life span. **Dr Marie Mills** (dementia care practitioner and research fellow at the University of Southampton) describes a piece of research in which, using a combination of reminiscence and counselling, she interviewed older people with dementia several times during a two-year period. She described how knowledge of a past life can continue to contribute to care delivery as people's capabilities change and people experience 'loss of personal narrative'. The third speaker, **Derek Clifford**, lecturer in the School of Law, Social Work and Social Policy at Liverpool John Moores University, drew on highly contrasting sources for his contribution: a computerised approach in child care assessment. Using an oral history approach to social work assessment is, he argues, invaluable for social workers who need to develop an understanding of the lives of oppressed groups in society. His computerised approach to oral and life history work draws on a diagrammatic presentation of, and provides the basis for, biographical assessments.

REFERENCES

Adams, J., Bornat, J. and Prickett, M. (1996) '"You wouldn't be interested in my life, I've done nothing": care planning and life history work with frail older women' in Phillips, J. and Penhale, B. (eds) *Reviewing Care Management for Older People*, London: Jessica Kingsley.

Bornat, J., Dimmock, B., Jones, D. and Peace, S. (1998) 'Care in the "new" family: changing contexts for traditional obligations' in Silva, E. and Smart, C. (eds) *The 'New' Family?*, London: Sage.

Bornat, J. (1989) 'Oral history as a social movement: reminiscence and older people', *Oral History*, Autumn: 16-24.

Boulton, J., Gully, V., Matthews, L. and Gearing, B. (1989), *Developing the Biographical Approach in Practice with Older People*, Care of elderly people at home, Project Paper 7, Buckingham: The Open University and Policy Studies Institute.

Butler, R.N. (1963) 'The life review: an interpretation of reminiscence in the aged', *Psychiatry* 26: 65-76.

Coleman, P.G. (1986) *Ageing and Reminiscence Processes: social and clinical implications*, Chichester: Wiley.

Dant, T. and Gully, V. (1994) *Co-ordinating Care at Home*, London: Collins.

Gibson, F. (1993)'What can reminiscence contribute to dementia?', in Bornat, J. (ed) *Reminiscence Reviewed: perspectives, evaluations, achievements*, Buckingham: Open University Press.

Haight, B.K. and Webster, J.D. (eds) (1995) *The Art and Science of Reminiscing: theory, research, methods and applications*, Washington: Taylor and Francis.

Johnson, M.L. (1976) 'That was your life: a biographical approach to later life' in Munnichs, J.M.A. and van den Heuvel, W.J.A. (eds) *Dependency and Interdependency in Old Age*, The Hague: Martinus Nijhoff.

CARER BIOGRAPHIES
Implications for Practice

PRUE CHAMBERLAYNE
Centre for Biography in Social Policy, University of East London.

One of the themes of the Cultures of Care project[1] has been to explore how underlying family strategies and family histories influence caring situations. As a comparative project, it has also been concerned to show how caring strategies and situations are shaped by welfare and social systems. This paper describes the methodology of the biographical-interpretive method which was used in the study, and then briefly presents two case studies. These concern the care of young rather than elderly people, but have a wide relevance to caring. The first shows a trajectory in which a strategy of family closure for many years seals off recourse to outside support, and 'opening' only occurs much later. In the second case, the main carer who has long escaped and then resisted her family's historical pattern of female domestic entrapment, increasingly succumbs to it in the context of service inadequacy. In the third section, the paper discusses the relevance of the method to professionals, issues of ethics and empowerment, and possible ways of developing the usefulness of the method through collaboration.

THE METHOD

The method, which is based on phenomenology, starts with an open narrative interview in which the subject is asked to speak freely about his or her own situation. The idea is to encourage the person to explore, reconstruct and re-live experiences within his or her own frame of reference. Much of the time the person will be rationalising and legitimating their activities, as well as reporting actions and events and describing situations, and in so doing they will shift between past, present and future perspectives. They will draw on a mix of more public and more personal views. The role of the interviewer is to be an active listener, avoiding any interruption of the initial free-flowing narrative account, which may last anything from a few minutes to several hours.

The opening question in this study invited carers to talk about how their caring situation started and then developed, what support they had and would have liked to have had, and what caring meant for them personally. In the second stage of the interview, the interviewer asked questions which kept to the thematic sequence of the initial account, encouraging further recall within that frame. Only in the third stage were 'external' questions posed, to cover outstanding research themes.

The interpretation of the interview begins with a separate analysis of the 'lived' and the 'told' life. These are then compared to arrive at the 'case structure', or the 'structuring principle' which underlies the interview text. First, all the life events mentioned in the interview are taken out and ordered chronologically, sometimes as a genogram. This sequence of biographical data is then interpreted item by item, through a process of hypothesising about what options could have been taken, which highlights the pattern of choices which were made.

In a parallel exercise, the structure of the interview text is analysed step-by-step to discern the underlying pattern in the construction of the self-presentation and in the reconstruction of the experiences. The order of the themes and the broader thematic fields they belong to are analysed, together with the narrative style and time perspectives which are being used. The method is premised on both action and gestalt approaches, the idea that every life event or utterance involves selection, and also that there are coherent patterns, even 'rules', being followed in the way lives are both led and reconstructed in narrative (Rosenthal 1993; Chamberlayne and King 1996).

TWO CASE STUDIES

These case studies are taken from the Cultures of Care British study, and both are from Newham. They illustrate opposite patterns of family closure and openness to service support, and they undergo opposite changes of orientation to the past and the future.

The first concerns an Asian carer, Mrs Rajan, whose response to giving birth to a severely disabled son was to move back into her family of origin's strategy of closure. Only eleven years later, following the birth of a healthy son, did she begin to accept help from outside, become involved in community activities, and adopt an orientation to the future. The 'family strategy' belonged specifically to her family, which during her childhood in East Africa kept its family of daughters tightly enclosed in the private sphere, also keeping secret the mother's epilepsy. Coming to the Midlands in the 1970s at the age of 12, there were plenty of opportunities for her to leave this strategy. Much of Mrs Rajan's schooling was in Britain, her sisters trained professionally, she herself worked in a shop, and although she married at 18, she moved away from her own family. Moreover, her in-law family expected a more modern nuclear family life style. However, she had two children in rapid succession, both of whom were sickly. The boy was soon diagnosed by the hospital as likely to die, although when the parents fatalistically took him home, he was nursed back to health by Mrs Rajan's mother, using traditional Indian methods.

For the next ten years it seems that Mrs Rajan scarcely left the house. She quarrelled with her mother-in-law, cutting off the little support that family offered, and cast herself as 'forbidden' to leave the children by her husband. It is clear that she was not open to discussion or intervention. Her third pregnancy only came to term in defiance of her own actions. Advised at seven months to have a termination (following a much delayed diagnosis of genetic disorder in the first son, for what seems likely to have been a vaccination problem), she starved herself. By now the older boy was boisterously resisting her strategy of confinement, and with the prospect of three children to handle, she clearly more pressingly needed outside help. Doubtless more professionals came in contact with the family through the new pregnancy.

Nevertheless, it seems likely that the birth of a healthy son became a turning point which set her on a new course, giving her confidence to appear and engage in the outside world. She now accepts respite care for the older boy, has long discussions with the social worker in which her own and her husband's views are recognised and negotiated, and she works as an ancillary worker in the school, where, according to her children, she is very good at playing with children. She participates in festivities in the community, the headmistress is encouraging her to train as a nursery nurse, and she is planning the future care of her disabled son. The shift is paralled in the interview itself, in which she switches from a long, monosyllabic period of huddling in her chair, head in hands, into an eventual free-flowing account of her experiences.

Mrs Buckley comes from a large, white, working-class family in which women go on having children into their forties, and older girls are greatly involved in the care of younger siblings. In order to escape this pattern, Mrs Buckley entered a mobile professional career which involved much travel, and avoided having children until well into her thirties. Even after Melanie was born disabled Mrs Buckley continued to work, and this was encouraged and facilitated by staff at Great Ormond Street Hospital. A spiral developed, however, in which each time she and her husband firmly adopted some new measure of independence, Melanie plunged back into a new stage of illness and dependency.

To a great extent the increasing dependency between Mrs Buckley and Melanie is structured by external events: as a young woman with gynaecological problems Melanie cannot be tended by her father, at home or in public, in the way she used to be; the adult services are a great deal more partial than school provision; service cuts exacerbate this, and the residential options seem dubious. Yet, 'objectively' speaking, Mrs Buckley's family tradition has reclaimed her. For while she fears that no public service will love and understand Melanie in the way she does, her husband advocates supported independent living. He wants to plan their future lives and retirement, but she cannot look beyond the present.

In a fuller account of these two cases, Rupp and Jones (1997) compare the pattern of life events with the structure of the narrative text, which is necessary to demonstrate the way the case structure is arrived at. My presentation here focuses on the life events, but I hope it nevertheless shows that unreflected family strategies and family histories can influence current coping strategies in a decisive way, blocking the carer's capacity to create new strategies and solutions. In fact, a key finding of the study is that, in comparison with either East or West Germany, the fragmented and uncertain nature of services over time in Britain means that carers are more likely to be thrown back into such family traditions (King 1997).

PROFESSIONAL RELEVANCE

We feel convinced that the biographical-interpretive method offers insights which could be of great value to professionals in understanding and planning interventions into caring situations, but also to carers and disabled people themselves. However, the emphasis on the interpretation of underlying meanings and dynamics in this form of biographical work does complicate issues of feedback and requires collaboration with professionals, as was extensively discussed at the seminar. Reaching the method's full potential for empowering both carers and disabled people to disentangle their separate interests and tackle issues of power and dependency in caring relationships would likewise usually require professional support.

The differentiation in the method between the 'objective' pattern of lived events and their 'subjective' reconstruction already offers a vantage point for professional interventions. Parallel with this is the distinction between 'personal' and 'system' dynamics, which appears much more clearly in the comparative work than in single cases. Personal and social structural levels are strongly interactive, but strategies of intervention need to distinguish them, and to work at both (King and Chamberlayne 1996; Rupp and Jones 1997). Separating out such 'strands' in caring situations would also surely be of great assistance in negotiating the separate interests of carers and disabled people.

As was suggested in the seminar discussion, the recognition of family structures questions the assumptions which are made in care planning about the 'autonomy of the individual' - or at least how easily such 'autonomy' can be realised, especially in cases of great physical and emotional dependency. In contrast with the claims of some sections of the disability lobby (Morris 1994), it seems unlikely that family traditions can be lightly shaken off, even when independent living is achieved. The renewed hold of the family strategy on Mrs Buckley, after decades of determined independence, illustrates this point.

By marking out the development and key turning points in the underlying dynamics of a caring situation, the method is strongly suggestive of the moments at which intervention would be possible, and of the obstacles which attempted interventions might encounter. Mrs Rajan's sealed-offness before the birth of her healthy son is rather graphic. The method can also identify situations of impending crisis, in which caring is rapidly becoming unsustainable. The contrasting of carer strategies can also enhance the appreciation of options among carers themselves. Carers often feel very constrained, not seeing the space for choice, or the ways different people would act in that situation.

In reply to the research question of how carers integrate caring into their biographies, we contrasted three patterns: change, continuity and 'switch' (Chamberlayne and King 1997). In the first category, change may have been an ongoing feature of the pre-caring life, but in others the caring brings about a new and significant change in the 'biographical cast' of the person, in the person's identity and view of their life. The centre of change may be located within the inner self through the emergence of the changed or enhanced personality, or through the acquisition of new competence, or it occurs through a social repositioning in relation to employment, social activity, family or friends. In many cases change is constituted both internally and externally.

In the second category, carers accommodate caring into the parameters of their existing life orientation, their life style and life course. The sense of self of such carers does not seem to have altered through the caring experience in a significant way. Here carers draw on their pre-caring life to adapt to a new situation, often recreating the past in the present. It may be that someone who has had a traditional, highly gendered servicing role in the family thinks that they can take on the additional caring, however onerous, and that calling in outside services constitutes a threat to the sense of self. A person who is resistant to outside forms of help may be actively, even aggressively, resisting change. In the third category, people are torn between competing or parallel biographical courses and identities. These are often the newer carers, who are still in a mobile situation, and it may be that it is in such early stages of a caring career that intervention could be most helpful, as indeed crisis intervention theory would suggest concerning bereavement.[2]

The two case studies represent examples of opposite shifts between continuity and change. They also involve opposite patterns of relationship with the past and the future, which is another point of focus in the method that may be of great use in professional practice. For a turning point in a trajectory is often a re-shaping of a present situation, a changing of expectations of the future, perhaps a changing of understandings of the past, a re-storying of the life or particular aspects of it. Identifying and understanding turning points, and helping to bring them about, can be of great help. Indeed, individuals who enter personal therapy often feel at the end of the road, and what goes on is a new connecting between past and future, an opening up of a new future by re-exploring the past. Such a reconstructive process goes on in much daily conversation, and in the interview process itself, and it may explain why respondents enjoy narrative interviews so much. It is undoubtedly part of professional practice, at least in situations where traditional case work is still possible.

The biographical-interpretive method explores underlying dynamics in interpersonal situations, and makes an interpretation of a case that would not necessarily be acceptable to the interviewee. In several important respects this challenges the established ethics of life history methods, such as the sharing of findings with the respondent for purposes of empowerment, and the incorporation of feedback in the report process in a process of coproduction. The dilemma with this particular method of biographical work is how to realise its empowering potential while respecting the sensitivity of the material. The results are often much too painful to be straightforwardly fed back; feedback could only take place in a context of professional support, with people who wanted to work through such issues.[3] The professionals, themselves, would need to understand the method and be convinced of its useful potential for their own work. Our conclusion is that future work must involve ongoing collaboration with professionals, and we would hope through such cooperation to explore ways of developing the method, or aspects of it, for professional practice.

It is also important to separate out feedback to individual interviewees and to a wider constituency of carers. Anonymisation is difficult with case study material in which particularities are of the essence; the best we can do is to change key features of the case after the completion of the analysis, at least to make the case unrecognisable to others. Making changes before that point would change the case structure, so that the involvement of interviewees themselves in analytical workshops is ruled out. Discussing completed results in focus groups is possible, however, and feeding the results into carer organisations and thus into the public discourse of caring is also empowering.

As Joanna Bornat notes in the introduction, the ESRC project on step-families showed that people are often hunting and searching for explanations of change in their life through talk. In future work, we may well find individuals who do want to discuss the interpretation of their case with us, and even some who are willing to present the dynamics of their case in the public arena, in order to help others, and perhaps to gain public validation. Moreover, in an important sense the interpretation is coproduced, in that it may be suggested implicitly in the way people are thinking and re-thinking and re-formulating their lives as they are talking - indeed the method centres exactly on that, the construction and reconstruction of lives in narrative accounts. Besides, the very giving of an interview is a trustful act of speaking to the public world via the research.

Our overwhelming impression from talking to professionals is that the method resonates strongly with traditional case work methods, which have all too often been marginalised by the new managerialism. Whether the procedures of biographical-interpretive methods can be made practicably useful to professionals in developing strategies for intervention, and in helping families members recognise and negotiate their family histories and dynamics, remains to be tested. Many professionals have expressed enthusiasm for such collaboration.

NOTES

1. The Cultures of Care project used biographical methods to compare informal caring in East and West Germany and Britain. It was funded by the ESRC (R000233921) from 1992-5, and by the University of East London 1995-7. The German fieldwork was conducted by Prue Chamberlayne and Annette King, together with local interviewers, who were trained by local consultants (Martina Schiebel and Simone Kreher). The British research was conducted by Frauke Ruppel, Susanne Rupp and Christine Jones. Annette King played a key role in the interpretation work of both studies.

2. Discussions with social work colleagues, especially Wendy Cree, have been important in developing such ideas.

3. The German study has helped us to think through these issues, but has not itself resolved them. The geographical distance from Germany, and the fact that the British study had to parallel the German one created seemingly unsurmountable difficulties. A feedback visit, for which a pamphlet had specially been prepared, gave rise to valuable discussions with academics and researchers, but failed to mobilise the front-line professionals, whose specific advice we needed.

REFERENCES

Chamberlayne, P. and King, A. (1996) 'Biographical approaches in comparative work: the Cultures of Care Project' in Hantrais, L. and Mangen, S. (eds) *Cross-National Research Methods in the Social Sciences*, London: Pinter.

Chamberlayne, P. and King, A. (1997) 'The Biographical Challenge of Caring', *The Sociology of Health and Illness*, 19(5): 601-21.

King, A. and Chamberlayne, P. (1996) 'Comparing the informal sphere: public and private relations of welfare in East and West Germany', *Sociology* 30(4): 741-61.

King, A. (1997) 'The British case: sitting on the doorstep'. Working paper for Cultures of Care project.

Morris, J. (1994)'Community Care or Independent Living?', *Critical Social Policy* 40: 24-45.

Rosenthal, G. (1993) 'Reconstruction of life stories: principles of selection in generating stories for narrative biographical interviews' in Josselson, R. and Lieblich, A. (eds) *The Narrative Study of Lives*, London: Sage.

Rupp, S. and Jones, C. (1997) 'Coping with caring: lives of informal carers in Newham', *Rising East: the Journal of East London Studies* 1(2):89-110.

3

USING THE NARRATIVE IN DEMENTIA CARE

MARIE A MILLS

Dementia Care Practitioner and Research Fellow
University of Southampton

INTRODUCTION

In recent years our understanding of the use of life story/reminiscence work with demented elderly people has grown considerably. Theorists and practitioners have attested to its efficacy in different areas of dementia care. Bornat (1994), Bornat and Adams (1992) have argued that it helps to assess need in this client group. Bender (1994) suggests that reminiscence is an enjoyable activity and Gibson (1994) points to life history work as having therapeutic implications for the sufferers of dementia and their carers.

In addition, Mills and Coleman (1994) argue that reminiscence and counselling strategies are effective in allowing dementing elderly people to recall safely aspects of their past. Moreover, Coleman and Mills (1997) have found that older people who were depressed and dementing experienced well-being through telling their stories to an experienced and attentive listener.

Nonetheless, a review of the reminiscence literature suggests that much of the published work has clouded research issues (Haight 1991), with a lack of experimental evidence (Bornat 1994). However, a more recent review (Haight and Hendrix 1995: 8) indicates a greater clarity in descriptions and methodologies 'with the value of the life story appreciated'. Longitudinal studies of observed and evaluated reminiscence have been scarce. One notable exception has been Coleman's ten-year study of older people living in London, some of whom had dementia (Coleman 1986). Further, Bornat (1989) and Coleman (1994) argue that reminiscence is not beneficial to all older people. Coleman (1994: 17) suggests that, 'We need to examine reminiscence in a variety of contexts and cultures. Much will change with the attitude of the listener.' Thus, there is a need for more longitudinal evidence in this field. Aims, objectives and methodology should be clearly defined, together with an explanation of the reminiscence role itself. In addition, previous arguments highlight the importance of interviewing/listening skills if painful memories should emerge. My own research tried to apply these precepts to a longitudinal study of narrative recall in dementia (Mills 1995, 1997a).

Reminiscence theory points to the intertwined relationship between life and story (Widdershoven, 1993). The whole is, of course, supported by memory. Dementia compromises recall, but it is argued that autobiographical memories with their associated emotions have greater endurance than semantic memory (Conway 1990). Further, as Knight (1986) has commented, the counselling interview is comprised of autobiographical memories and life evaluation.

A STUDY OF THE NARRATIVE IN DEMENTIA

Thus, using a combined reminiscence and counselling approach, which was based on personal training, experience and evaluation (Mills 1991, 1992) eight dementing elderly people were interviewed over a two-year period. These people who were aged between 65 and 85 years attended an NHS psychogeriatric day centre. The charge nurse in the setting selected the informants, the only interviewer criteria being that informants were able to speak, and would enjoy discussing their past with another person in a one to one situation. The local ethical committee for research approved the investigation, together with the psychogeriatrician, hospital staff and relatives. After our initial meeting, informants, too, were always asked if they wished to take part prior to each interview. None ever refused to speak to me, although some interviews were less lengthy than others. Informants themselves dictated the topic, pace and length of each meeting. We normally met each week, with many interviews being recorded and transcribed. The number of interviews with each informant varied between thirteen and twenty five. The total number of recorded and transcribed interviews was 141.

The 740 pages of data were analysed using case-study methods (Bromley 1986;

Runyan 1982; Yin 1989) and grounded theory (Glaser and Strauss 1967). This analysis indicated that all informants were able to recall fragmented but significant pieces of a personal past which gradually cohered into a more complete life story, although psychological testing indicated that memory was often severely compromised. Using Wong and Watt's (1991) taxonomy of reminiscence, the type that was common to all informants was that of narrative reminiscence. Further, these memories were generally concerned with highly emotional topics. They were the type of memories which, as one male informant said, 'Live long in the memory of a mind.'

All informants displayed increased levels of well-being, even as their cognitive abilities declined. This finding was supported by staff in the setting. However, as Coleman (1994) points out, the use of reminiscence with the aged requires sensitivity. It was found that simple reminiscences could frequently spill over into life review, which has psychotherapeutic implications. All informants reviewed their life at times and for some of them this was a painful, albeit therapeutic, process. Coleman and Mills (1997), Conway (1990) and Mills (1997b) argue that the links between memory and emotion are very strong. There is also a growing interest in the use of psychotherapeutic interventions with demented elderly people which focuses on past and present concerns (Hausman 1992; Mills 1992; Sinason 1992; Sutton 1994).

THE VOICES OF THE INFORMANTS

Space does not permit an in-depth discussion of the findings but some examples may underline theoretical and practical positions. One informant was able to recall a traumatic childhood where he suffered physical abuse at the hands of a brutal stepfather:

Cause it was a very hard life when I was a kid anyway...Oh yes! Hit about terrible!...Yes. Drunken father...stepfather...terrible man!

A female informant with moderate dementia spoke often of her deceased mother and her bad temper. She frequently spoke of her mother as if she was still alive. However, she was finally able to say that she was glad when her mother died, even though her mother had been unkind to her she felt that this was a terrible thing to admit:

I mean, well it's an awful thing to have to say isn't it, about your own mother?
Little things come back in my mind every now and again, you know, and it was ' What are you doing up here? You'll have to go on downstairs out of the way. I can't be troubled with you!' And things like that, you know. I mean, it hurts!

Another male informant, with impaired speech, was able to give some understanding of his anger and grief at being separated from his wife during a period of necessary respite care:

*Interviewer: **And you feel angry?***
I do! Very ! Very!... N N N N I can't can't can't do d told. I I I not not not said! I've never seen la seen er ... [his wife]...and anything else! And that's what's on on on my my my bad head! (*He sounded extremely frustrated and very sad. *)

On a more practical level, biographical knowledge of informants allowed some behaviours to become more comprehensible. A retired manager of a large department store seemed to be very unsettled at the beginning of the day. However, when the interviewer realised that he saw the female care staff as shop assistants, who were standing around talking to each other and not getting on with their work, his behaviour became very clear. Further, he felt a strong loss of autonomy:

*Interviewer: **Well you're used to being in charge aren't you?***
Oh yes! Well that's it's gone from glory hasn't it?

DISCUSSION

Many practitioners may feel uneasy with a seemingly indiscriminate 'rummaging' in the memories of frail and dementing elderly, and will wish to establish firm guidelines for practice. Coleman and Mills (1997) suggest certain principles for care practice which include ethical and training issues. As Challis and Davies (1986) argue, it is professional carers who frequently become the major confidante for those in their care. Certainly, spontaneous life review may occur when personal care needs are being met. Carers, therefore, should be trained in empathetic listening, but made aware that some life-review situations may require greater expertise.

However, the study of Haight *et al.* (1995) found that older people significantly benefited from speaking of painful past experiences to professional home carers. Thus, there is a need to establish if this work can only be undertaken by the trained professional such as social workers, counsellors or psychologists whose expertise includes working with older clients. It would be a great tragedy if staff felt constrained to deny the right of older people with dementia to speak of troubling memories. Undoubtedly some of these fragmented memories of the past can intrude into the present. Stokes (1996) gives several examples of how knowledge of the narrative of dementing clients enables professional carers to interpret and ameliorate upsetting behaviours in residential units.

Further, knowledge of the narrative of older people in residential care promotes well-being (Gibson 1994; Mills 1997a). Vignettes from a specialist private residential care home for twenty older people with dementia, and with many years of service by care staff, give support to this argument. Among the residents are those who have experienced a loss of personal narrative. Yet present residents give every indication of experiencing states of well-being. One, who has been resident for five years, will tell carers that she loves them and hugs her soft cuddly toy given by her daughter. If noisy, she becomes calmer when staff speak and gently stroke her face, or hold her hand. She appears to listen when they are speaking.

Another tiny elderly lady has been a resident for nine years. She is immobile but sits in her chair, constantly moving her head and arms, whilst chuckling and laughing to herself. She gives every indication of enjoying the experience of touch, and will stroke fabrics with signs of great pleasure. Given their length of service, most carers have had a long relationship with these two residents. Further, staff knew them when they were less incapacitated, and they are aware of their previous history and preferences. In this sense, the personal narrative of each of these residents has been retained and held by those who care for them.

A further nine residents, who are in a state of narrative dissolution due to the dementing process, also exhibit signs of well-being, albeit to varying degrees. Again, many have been resident for some years and staff were able to recall parts of their narratives without recourse to their personal records. They spoke of one peaceful and loving lady aged 95 years who cared for her deceased blind husband with great devotion for many years. She frequently approached staff to give them gentle pats and hugs which were reciprocated.

One other resident had been a professional actress. Staff knew the London theatres where she had appeared and the lead parts she had played. They also knew of the Guernsey tea shop that she and her husband had kept after retirement, and the many hundreds of scones she made each day for visitors to the island. She remembers to this day how much she disliked doing this. This particular resident has also allowed her carers to have a glimpse of what helps the dementia sufferer to achieve well-being in dementia.'Things don't matter,' she said, 'People matter, and good kindness.'

CONCLUSION

If these people live long enough, they will eventually experience a total dissolution of narrative, and the corresponding loss of narrative identity, prior to death. Thus, the retention of their narrative gives carers respect and understanding of the needs, emotions and behaviours of dementia sufferers, which is so necessary in dementia care work. This understanding enables the maintenance of well-being and personhood. Life story work with demented elderly people, therefore, is a shared discourse and a creative interactive process.

However this process is defined it remains an integral part of good dementia care work. Indeed, as one of the informants in Goldsmith's study commented, 'Knowledge of the narrative of the other *is* knowledge of the other' (Goldsmith 1996: 88). Goldsmith, himself, argues that it is our responsibility to hear the voice of people with dementia, although 'normal professional qualifications and usual work practices seldom equip us for this task, but it is a voice that is quite literally crying out to be heard' (p.165). Coleman and Mills (1997) suggest that listening to the voice of dementia is possible for all of us. It remains one of the crucial tasks in dementia care work.

REFERENCES

Bender, M. (1994) 'An interesting confusion: what can we do with reminiscence group work?' in Bornat, J. (ed.) *Reminiscence Reviewed: perspectives, evaluations, achievements,* Buckingham: Open University Press.

Bornat, J. (1989) 'Oral history as a social movement: reminiscence and older people', *Oral History* 17(2): 16-24.

Bornat, J. (1994) 'Introduction' in Bornat, J. (ed.) *Reminiscence Reviewed: perspectives, evaluations, achievements,* Buckingham: Open University Press.

Bornat, J. and Adams, J. (1992) 'Models of biography and reminiscence in the nursing care of frail elderly people' in Via, J. M. and Portella, E. (eds) *Proceedings of the 4th International Conference on Systems Science in Health Social Services for the Elderly and Disabled,* Vol.11, Barcelona: A. Camps.

Bromley, D.B. (1986) *The Case-Study Method in Psychology and Related Disciplines,* Chichester: John Wiley.

Challis, D. and Davies, B.H. (1986) *Case Management in Community Care,* Aldershot: Gower.

Coleman, P. G. (1986) *Ageing and Reminiscence Processes: social and clinical implications, Chichester:* John Wiley.

Coleman, P.G. and Mills, M.A. (1997) 'Listening to the story: life review in community and residential care settings' in Hunt, L., Marshall, M. and Rowlands, C.

(eds) *Past Trauma in Late Life: European perspectives on therapeutic work with older people*, London: Jessica Kingsley.

Coleman, P.G. (1994) 'Reminiscence within the sudy of ageing' in Bornat, J. (ed.) *Reminiscence Reviewed: perspectives, evaluations, achievements*, Buckingham: Open University Press.

Conway, M. (1990) *Autobiographical Memory: an introduction*, Buckingham: Open University Press.

Gibson, F. (1994) 'What can reminiscence contribute to people with dementia?' in Bornat, J. (ed.) *Reminiscence Reviewed: perspectives, evaluations, achievements*, Buckingham: Open University Press.

Glaser, B. and Strauss, A. (1967) *The Discovery of Grounded Theory: strategies for qualitative research*, Chicago: Aldine.

Goldsmith, M. (1996) *Hearing the Voice of People with Dementia: opportunities and obstacles*, London. Jessica Kingsley.

Haight, B.K. (1991) 'Reminiscing: the state of the art as a basis for practice', *International Journal of Ageing and Human Development* 33 (1): 1-32.

Haight, B.K. and Hendrix, S. (1995) 'An integrated review of reminiscence' in Haight, B.K. and Webster, J.D. (eds) *The Art and Science of Reminiscing: theory, research, methods, and applications,* London: Taylor and Francis.

Haight, B.K., Coleman, P.G. and Lord, K. (1995) 'The linchpins of a successful life review: structure, evaluation and individuality' in Haight, B.K. and Webster, J. D. (eds) *The Art and Science of Reminiscing: theory, research, methods, and applications*, London: Taylor and Francis.

Hausman, C. (1992) 'Dynamic psychotherapy with elderly demented patients' in Jones, G.M. and Miesen, B.M. (eds) *Care Giving in Dementia: research and applications*, London: Routledge.

Knight, B. (1986) *Psychotherapy with Older Adults*, Beverley Hills, CA: Sage

Mills, M.A. (1991) Making the Invisible Visible: a qualitative study in the use of reminiscence therapy and counselling skills with dementing elderly people. Unpublished Thesis, University of Bournemouth.

Mills, M.A. (1992) 'Dementia, reminiscence and counselling skills: a new approach', *Generations Review* 2(1): 7-9.

Mills, M.A. (1995) Narrative Identity and Dementia: a study of emotion and narrative in older people with dementia. PhD Thesis, University of Southampton

Mills, M.A. (1997a) 'Narrative identity and dementia: a study of emotion and narrative in older people with dementia', *Ageing and Society* 17(6): 673-98.

Mills, M.A. (1997b) 'Memory, dementia and emotion' in Jones, G.M. and Miesen, B.M. (eds) *Care-Giving in Dementia: research and applications*, Vol. 2, London:

Routledge.

Mills, M.A. and Coleman, P.G. (1994) 'Nostalgic memories in dementia: a case study', *International Journal of Aging and Human Development* 8 (3): 203-19.

Runyan, W.M (1982) *Life Histories and Psychobiography: explorations in theory and method*, Oxford: Oxford University Press.

Sinason, V. (1992) *Mental Handicap and the Human Condition: new approaches from the Taverstock*, London: Routledge.

Stokes, G. (1996) 'Challenging behaviour in dementia' in Woods, R. (ed.) *Handbook of the Clinical Psychology of Ageing*, Chichester: John Wiley.

Widdershoven, G.A.M. (1993) 'The story of life: hermeneutic perspectives on the relationship between narrative and life history' in Josselson, R. and Lieblich, A. (eds) *The Narrative Study of Lives*, London: Sage.

Wong, P.T. and Watt, L.M. (1991) 'What types of reminiscence are associated with successful aging?', *Journal of Psychology and Ageing* 6(2): 272-9.

Yin, R.K. (1989) *Case-Study Research: design and methods*. Applied Social Research Methods Series, 5. revised ed., London: Sage.

4

SOCIAL ASSESSMENT, BIOGRAPHICAL METHOD AND COMPUTERISED MAPPING

School of Law and Applied Social Work, Liverpool John Moores University

I was asked to contribute to a seminar at the Centre for Policy on Ageing although my background and interests are different but related to the theme of biographical methods in working with older people. As a social worker, I have worked in hospitals, area offices and clinics with a range of users. I now lecture in social work, and I am interested in oral history and biographical methods, because I see them as being of general importance in any attempt to understand the lives, needs and strengths of service users - at whatever age.

My main interests are in childcare, social assessment, and the inter-relationship between values and methods in practice and research. I have especially been interested in trying to work out how people, whose life experiences are framed by a specific set of experiences in historical time and social space, can possibly be fairly understood by others, whose lives have fallen into a different set of social and historical circumstances. I remember how, many years ago as a university educated, unqualified male medical social worker, I had to discuss what would be now described as a suitable 'package of care' with an ex-soldier who had fought in the Boer war. He did not say much, but it was clear that we certainly did not see things in the same way! Since then I have been increasingly aware of the many social divisions which separated my perceptions from those of others, including all the social divisions relating to ethnicity, gender, class, sexuality and disability.

I now value a biographical approach to social assessment generally as a useful basis for both theory and practice, precisely because it can be used to raise all the relevant issues in a way which helps both parties in a relationship (whether voluntary or professional) to understand how needs and strengths have been generated and are understood. I have been concerned to develop both the theory and practice of social assessment in this context and have written in a number of places about this theoretical basis (Clifford 1992/3, 1994, 1995; Clifford and Cropper 1994, 1997a,b). This is not just of academic importance in my view, first, because work in the health and social services generally is under-rated and underpaid (partly because it is largely a female area of work). Therefore, it is important to provide a strong underpinning to what nurses, social workers and others do, since it can involve just as intellectually complex and valid procedures as other activities and professions which have far higher social status and reward. Second, it is hoped that by clarifying the theory in relation with practice, both will benefit.

It is evident that assessment practice involves the use of many bureaucratic procedures, multiple checklists and forms, and recording and reporting techniques which vary in different settings. My argument is that underlying them all are key factors that need to be clearly understood if the process is to succeed in giving older people (or any other service user) a fair and appropriate service, and that these key factors closely relate to biographical understanding. However brief the relationship may be, however overloaded the worker, and however bureaucratic the process, these factors are always present, and the problem is always to judge how they are operating in a specific case, how that should affect the process and outcome, and what strategies might be effected to take account of them.

I have drawn these key factors from studying accounts of understanding social life that have been written by black and white women, and disabled, lesbian and working class women. I do not, therefore, take credit for presenting these factors, I simply think that attention should be drawn to the way in which they are highly compatible with, and contribute to, a biographical approach, and value the insight that they provide because of their access to experiences of discrimination and oppression. There is no way that they all agree in every detail, but I have been struck by what I understand as some of the commonalities. In particular the key factors that suggest a particular biographical approach include:

1. The importance of understanding a person in a context of changing and interacting social systems rather than seeing them as isolated individuals who happen to have specific problems in their own family histories.

2. The relevance of seeing that the worker or observer is also a participant in the relationship with specific life experience, values and perceptions which must affect the whole process.

3. The value of considering the whole range and interconnecting complexity of changing social divisions that may both separate and connect worker and user, and trying to understand the impact of social divisions on all the parties and systems in the process.

4. The significance of the changing structures and practices of power which affect the process and outcomes of intervention, at personal, organisational and wider social levels.

5. Contextualising medical, psychological and other histories into the social histories of those involved, and seeing the user, the worker and the process itself as having a specific place in time - a particular moment in their mutual biographies.

6. Overall is the basic principle of evaluating methods in the light of life experiences of discrimination and oppression by people who have them and have reflected upon them, providing distinctive perspectives on how their lives should be understood?

These factors all inter-relate and need to be taken together. They can be discussed as theoretical principles in the philosophy of the social sciences, but they are also issues of ethical and political importance for everyday social practice. The context of a biographical approach informed by these principles provides a basis for discussion and review for any particular form of assessment or intervention in people's lives, and I call it a 'critical auto/biographical' approach, a concept which is discussed much more fully elsewhere (Clifford 1998).

I found that these principles could be usefully summarised in the form of a diagram (see Diagram 1), and the way that the principles might be related to various kinds of practice in health and social welfare is also presented in a diagram (see Diagram 2). What I also found was that the subtleties of understanding a life and the process of assessment could be even better demonstrated if the original Diagram 1 could be expanded to show the multiple dimensions to which the different factors simultaneously refer. One of the black women writers I have studied, who has now published a number of works about oral history (Etter-Lewis 1991, 1996), expressed the view that a black woman's perspective could best be expressed through oral history precisely because her life history is 'multi-layered'. There were many aspects to her experiences – many stories which needed to be told.

Of course, a simple diagram cannot do justice to this complexity, so I have begun to develop a computerised version of the diagram, initially as a teaching tool, so that I can discuss the issues of theory and practice with students. I don't suppose for a minute that this method either will be able to catch all of the nuances and complexities of a real life situation. However, computer technology does have some advantages over two-dimensional paper diagrams. The computer software has been developed with the aid of technicians from the University where I work, and is now in its second version. It has been successfully used with students and with experienced social workers. They have said that it helps them to understand the issues more fully, and have thought it might at a later stage be used in actually making assessments or doing research.

The computer approach to understanding biographical research and assessment has the following significant advantages already built into the present version of the software, and other possibilities are being considered for future development. For instance, the horizontal axis of Diagram 1 represents time, and the life line of a person is drawn so as to correspond to the appropriate date on the time axis. However, there is a limit to how much time you can put on one page, unless you pack the years in very tightly. In that case there is not enough space to indicate significant events. In the computer version time on the vertical axis spreads for as far as you want it to go so that it can cover several generations of a family: it's like having an enormous time line on a sheet of wallpaper. You thus can 'scroll' across time to various points in a person's life, with the image on the screen moving smoothly to the desired historical date.

Similarly, the vertical axis on Diagram 2 represents social space, moving from individual lives at the top, downwards to extended family, peer groups, organisations and communities to the wider society. Obviously, on one page there are severe restrictions of space as to how much information you can usefully include. On the computer version it is possible to scroll down continuously through several pages where the individual life lines of relatives and significant friends may be represented, as well as collective 'life' lines representing organisations - so that the events affecting each are matched in terms of the date and time.

Enveloped within the collective life lines of organisations are individual life lines of specific workers who have been involved with the service user, who is the subject of study. However, one of these organisations is the employing agency of the worker who is responsible for the assessment. Thus the specific points of interaction between the organisations, the particular workers involved and the user can be represented, and the image on the screen changes as the cursor scrolls down through social space at a given point in time. This enables the viewer to see and consider the impact of interactions between the parties over time and through social space, including the relationship between the biography of the worker and the user.

What basically exists on the computer, therefore, is a very large life history 'map' with various bits of information about significant events and relationships marked on it. You can explore this map and evaluate the impact of events and relationships on people's lives, combining personal and family history with organisational, community and wider history. Membership of the various social divisions is indicated, and structure and practices of power between people, groups and organisations can be assessed. In relation to the service user it immediately offers the possibility of discussing, for example: risk factors; sources of strengths and needs; how and why problems, values and perspectives have developed and changed over time; and how the involvement of workers and agencies have been conditioned by the interaction of people's biographies and the organisational and historical context of changing policies and priorities.

Additionally, the computer offers several other options such as the use of buttons which can be clicked to call up further information. The values and perspectives of the different people involved at different points in time can be accessed and brought to the screen. This is important not only in principle, for example in representing the voice of the user, but also because it introduces the subjective perceptions of all those involved into the framework, thus qualifying the apparent objectivity of the time lines. At the moment, this is done crudely by means of text which reports what someone said at a particular time. However, one of the plans for future development is that it is possible to call up mini-videos of the people concerned. As the computer is currently based on hypothetical characters, this will involve the use of actors who will speak directly to you to say what they think about some aspect of their situation – including carers who put their point-of-view, and workers who speak from their particular setting at a period of contact with the user and the family.

Another currently available option is to 'zoom' into a much closer examination of a given period of time, so that crucial events can be unpacked and examined more carefully. Plans for the future include suggestions made by students and social workers who have tried the current version. Especially important will be the integration of checklists and notepads so that computer users can make their own notes about the information available, and compare the information they have obtained from exploring the life map with the various criteria and indicators of need and risk.

There is also the possibility of linking up directly or indirectly with software packages of research evidence on risk, so that the computer user can consider their own assessment against what is currently known about the indicators they have identified as relevant to this example. We have done this in the case of assessing risks to children and families by means of switching to a currently available (and separately purchased) package on research into evidence about child abuse.

The life history computer software originated as a general tool to understand the principles of biographical assessment in relation to understanding lives and needs. As far as I am concerned the most important point is not the sophistication of the technology. This may, I hope, turn out to be modestly useful as an effective teaching aid. It might even develop further as an assessment or research tool. However, what matters most to me is to be able to understand and discuss more easily the application of the above principles which seem to me to underlie all assessment - however constrained by the chaotic circumstances of real life caseloads, relationships, and (lack of) time.

The value of such an underpinning methodological framework is that it helps to ensure that an assessment is in principle based on a comprehensive, well-grounded approach to understanding life circumstances, which is sensitive to the complexities of differences between people, the realities of historical time and place, and the ethical and political factors affecting judgements and decision-making.

NOTE
The life history software was presented at the Social Services and Learning Technologies conference, University of Bournemouth, 17-18 July 1997. Anyone wanting to view the software should contact the author: Derek Clifford, Senior Lecturer in Social Work, School of Law and Applied Social Studies, Liverpool John Moores University, 1 Myrtle St, Liverpool L7 4DN.

REFERENCES
Clifford, D. (1992/3) 'Towards an anti-oppressive social work assessment method', *Practice* 6(3).

Clifford, D. (1994) 'Critical life histories: a key anti-oppressive research method' in Humphries, B. and Trueman, C. (eds) *Rethinking Social Research*, London: Avebury.

Clifford, D. (1995) 'Methods in oral history and social work', *Oral History* 24(2).

Clifford, D. and Cropper, A. (1994) 'Applying auto/biography: researching the assessment of life experiences', *Auto/Biography* 3(1/2): 47-58.

Clifford, D. and Cropper, A. (1997a) 'Individual assessment of potential carers: essential methods', *Practice* 9(1).

Clifford, D. and Cropper, A. (1997b) 'Parallel processes in researching and assessing potential carers', *Child and Family Social Work* 2(3).

Clifford, D. (1998) *Social Assessment Theory and Practice: a multi-disciplinary framework,* Aldershot: Ashgate.

Etter-Lewis, G. (1991) 'Black women's stories: reclaiming self in narrative texts' in Gluck, S.B. and Patai, D. (eds) *Women's Words: the feminist practice of oral history,* London: Routledge.

Etter-Lewis, G. (1996) *Unrelated Kin: race and gender in women's personal narratives,* London: Routledge.

A Critical Auto/Biographical Framework for Social Assessment (Diagram 1)

Oral histories/life stories of individuals, and significant others (represented by life lines), psychological development contextualised by an historically based life course sociology focusing on the social divisions, with an auto/biographically located observer/assessor

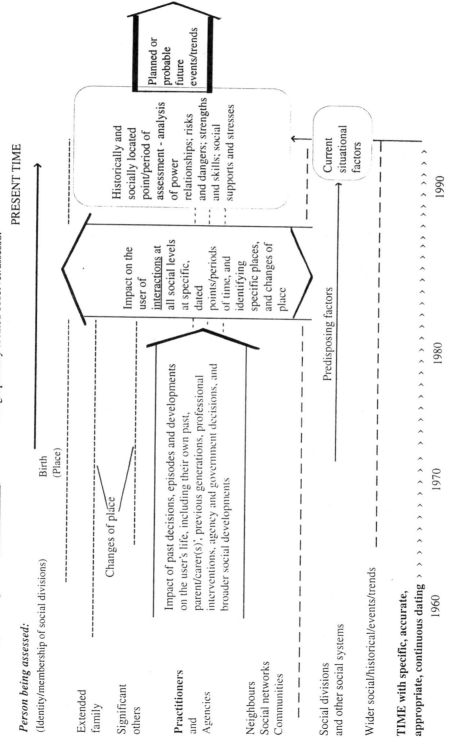

Person being assessed:

(Identity/membership of social divisions)

PRESENT TIME

Birth
(Place)

Extended family

Significant others

Changes of place

Practitioners and Agencies

Impact of past decisions, episodes and developments on the user's life, including their own past, parent/carer(s)', previous generations, professional interventions, agency and government decisions, and broader social developments

Neighbours
Social networks
Communities

Impact on the user of interactions at all social levels at specific, dated points/periods of time, and identifying specific places, and changes of place

Historically and socially located point/period of assessment - analysis of power relationships; risks and dangers; strengths and skills; social supports and stresses

Planned or probable future events/trends

Current situational factors

Social divisions and other social systems

Predisposing factors

Wider social/historical/events/trends

TIME with specific, accurate,
appropriate, continuous dating >

1960   1970   1980   1990

Applying a Research Methodology to Assessment (Diagram 2)

Complex Assessment

Multi-professional and multi-disciplinary assessment of multiple levels of need

Critical Auto/Biography as the context and critical framework for all aspects of assessment throughout the process
PLUS
specific review at key decision points within the process for:

<u>Different Methods:</u>
Methods have to be considered in relation to BOTH the type of assessment, and critically linked to the methodology

CHECKS on:
1. Terms, assumptions and procedures
2. Ambiguities, judgements, decisions
3. Relationships and outcomes
.. in terms of checklist of critical auto/biographical principles

<u>Types of assessment:</u>
Different types will vary with the function and purpose of the agency/agencies, and the rights and needs of the service users.
Having a specific focus, whether more or less comprehensive, they must be contextualised within the methodological framework as time-limited and partial accounts of people's lives

Understanding and values of assessing worker need to be consistent with critical auto/biog methodology: supervision and review should include (above):

Checklists of specific needs and requirements in relation to agency functions and resources

Simple Assessment

Critical Auto/Biographical Methodology

5

DISCUSSION
Joanna Bornat

The audience for the seminar included teachers and trainers in higher and further education, social work and nursing practitioners, as well as full-time researchers. Each of the papers provoked a lively discussion and in this final section of the report we have attempted to reproduce some of the main points which emerged. The whole seminar was recorded on tape and then transcribed so that what follows draws directly from what was said at the time. However, to make the discussion easier to follow, and to make the most of what were some important and well-made contributions, we have highlighted particular themes, edited the discussion and introduced sub-headings.

INTERVIEWS

Prue Chamberlayne's experience has been that people enjoy their interviews and are keen for a follow up. Similarly, Marie Mills' work with people with dementia suggested to her that there is a need for people to be heard but also that it may be necessary to find different ways of working when there are different forms of dementia.

There may be a need for a degree of flexibility in terms of the contexts where the interview takes place. Marie Mills described people choosing their own room, the hospital grounds, or even being on the move if they are 'in a pacey mood'. More often, it is a question of sitting down together. She always feels as if she is going off on a journey with someone, never knowing where she will end up.

Too rigid an approach to questioning can be off-putting. The researchers involved in the Gloucester project (see introduction to this report) found that the schedules they first adopted were too rigid and were inhibiting to the older people they interviewed. Eventually they adopted an approach which was more flexible and which allowed the interviewees more control over the process of talking.

Sometimes it isn't always clear how the interviewee perceives the interviewer, is it as researcher, social worker, nurse, perhaps as a mate? It may be that in real terms the process turns the interviewer into an advocate for the person being interviewed.

Several participants contributed their own feelings and experiences of taking part in interviews where there were traumatic memories. Sometimes an interviewer may find it difficult to listen to what they are being told and then, when it comes to transcribing, those bad experiences have to be heard again. Interviewers need help with learning to cope with what they hear, particularly if what they hear is repeated over again by people who have a dementing illness. Supervision is important for people listening to painful memories.

Good interviewing can mean drawing on a repertoire of counselling skills based in 'do no harm' and listening. If there is something which sounds unresolved, then it may be necessary to get permission from the interviewee to talk to somebody else. The difficulty of being a researcher and a practitioner was raised by someone who says she finds it difficult, when life history interviewing, to 'lose my hat as a health visitor'. For her there was a need to be objective when she was being a researcher but even so she couldn't help being 'tinged with compassion'.

ANALYSIS AND INTERPRETATION OF LIFE HISTORY INTERVIEW MATERIAL

Prue Chamberlayne's very detailed and painstaking method of interviewing raised issues relating to meeting immediate needs and disempowerment for the interviewee. The method described takes a long time when it comes to analysing the interview data and this could be a disincentive for workers and service users with urgent needs to be met. There is also the possibility that by taking a highly theoretical interpretive approach, interviewees might feel distanced from their own life stories. However, these long interviews offer the possibility of comparisons across the life span as the account of a whole life is drawn out.

There are dilemmas when it comes to dealing with the interpretation of the interview data. Prue Chamberlayne's first step, so far, has been to discuss this with the professionals and not the carers who were interviewed. In presenting the interpretation of the interview data to the carers they should be provided with support, particularly if there is a likelihood that they reject or deny the interpretations being offered.

Marie Mills' paper also led to a discussion around issues of analysis and interpretation, and how these can be introduced into practice settings. Conflicting statements raise issues of what is most important; if people are given opportunities to review their accounts, this can provide them with new insights into their own lives. Life history work could provide an opportunity for practitioners to sort out the historical from what is the subjective and this could be a helpful approach, serving to remind practitioners, such as nurses, that they are often making interpretive statements and decisions in the course of their daily work. The example of transition from home to hospital was given. Working with a life history approach could help the practitioner and the carer and service user to reflect on their immediate feelings in the context of their life experience together. In working with people with dementia there may be much repetition, but each time more information may emerge, providing a fuller picture.

The value of being able to counterpose a historical, structural framework to a more subjective account was a focus which developed in the discussion following Derek Clifford's paper. While there was general agreement that 'you can't leave reflexivity out', there was also a feeling that history and structure must also play a part if someone's account of their life is to be understood. It is possible that reflexivity could be taken too far. Though it is important for researchers and practitioners to include themselves into 'the equation', approaches which are 'free floating' in relation to historical context and structures such as race, gender and class sometimes go too far. History can be important in another way; knowledge about the past leads to role reversals, as the service user, or client, becomes the expert in the relationship with the practitioner. Derek gave an example of listening to a Liverpool-born black woman whose father had been imprisoned 'for his own safety' during the racist riots of 1919 in Liverpool. This was part of her biography, but previously unknown to him as an episode in the city's history.

There may be dangers of too literal acceptance of the historical record when what are perceived as universal experiences may in fact have led to quite different life experiences from what might have been expected. For example, the experience of men and women during the Second World War was in many cases quite different. Men's battlefield experiences might have been traumatising and their memories of separation and forces' discipline might be difficult. In contrast, many women remembered war-time as a period of excitement, high earnings and opportunities for unrestricted sexual encounters.

However, presenting someone with a multi-media package raises the possibility that they can develop their life story, with their own or publicly available images and that this could be added to a case file with a multi-stranded narrative showing the interconnections between their own and others' lives.

PRACTICAL ISSUES

Prue Chamberlayne saw the method she has worked with as having ultimate possibilities as a practical tool, one that might be used in tandem as an action research approach with researchers working together with practitioners and service users. Re-interpretation of the interview data could be used as a method of listening to how people are thinking and re-thinking their lives. This might lead to quite fruitful discussions for practitioners and for service users.

Using Marie Mill's approach might be helpful in working with people who have a dementing illness and who may lose their inhibitions or become depressed at a late stage. They might express anger about the last few years of their life, yet their earlier remembering may have been less emotional and accusatory. This could be helpful for carers.

In combination with a tool like Kitwood's Dementia Care Mapping (Kitwood, 1997: 46-7), reminiscence or biographical work could be used to provide a richer observational base for staff as 'without any life history it's impossible to care for people in an effective way'. Where people have dementia, it may be the case that the personal narratives live as long as the staff who work in a particular setting. They will remember what they have been told after the people they work with have forgotten. This raises issues for confidentiality and access to those accounts.

Some settings provide more challenges than others. So, for example, in hospital discharge it may be difficult to pass on to another practitioner what has been told. If someone has been in hospital for only a short time how far is it practicable or helpful to expect them to 'lift many veils'. However, community care may provide the real challenge, particularly where people have few visitors. For these contexts the Gloucester project could provide a useful model with its emphasis on biography as a basis for establishing and re-locating helpful local networks for care and support.

A social work focus on biographical interviewing draws attention to a focus on a biographical methodology rather than any one specific biographical method. Different types of assessment will be appropriate for different settings. There is a need as well to attend to the needs and rights of users as well as to the functions of the agency involved. Basically, this is an argument for a humanistic approach to social work methods and a political struggle against more managerialist methods. Advocating a biographical approach in working with service users is a question of legitimising talk about the self and of individual life experiences, enabling practitioners to get back in touch with why they are there and what the rewards of the job are.

EDUCATION AND TRAINING

There were various suggestions about the contribution which a biographical approach can make to education and training, from informal observation to more formal classroom settings. At one level the method could, as observation of one's own and other's practice, provide a basis for training in decision-making and reflection. At another quite personal level, autobiographical writing can be a way to get students to reflect on their own lives and to enthuse them about the detail and unexpected aspects to other people's lives which a life history approach can reveal. People can learn from seeing each other and from occupying different roles, as for example researchers or practitioners. This helps to improve techniques in biographical work, it also helps more broadly to identify commonalities across a range of appropriate skills.

Whether or not there should be different kinds of training for different occupational groups became a focus for discussion, a distinction being drawn between residential care workers who might be seeking a social work qualification and care assistants working in the private domiciliary care sector for whom qualifications might be unattainable. However, it was also pointed out that care groups share common ground, irrespective of whether or not they are working at degree, diploma or any other level. The same basic values are required.

With a multi-media approach comes the possibility that students can be helped to think in time and space and to develop multiple realities at the same time. This can be part of a process of helping students to understand that the practice of remembering may not always be what it at first appears to be. It may be a means to achieving a multi-layered understanding of the personal and political situations that people are in, a way of bringing a classic theme in anthropology and the social sciences to social work and care practice.

When it came to the question of qualifications there seemed to be unanimous agreement that the S/NVQ system has not helped biographical or reminiscence based approaches to become established amongst a repertoire of appropriate skills. One problem is that assessors tend to select items out of wider programmes and this tends to mean that the underlying philosophy may be fragmented and undermined. The process of assessment for S/NVQs means that only certain aspects of work may be seen as assessable, appropriate or necessary in caring. Yet without the validating stamp of NVQs, biographical approaches will not be seen as having legitimacy amongst care staff and their managers.

REFERENCE

Kitwood, T. (1997) *Dementia Reconsidered: the person comes first*, Buckingham: Open University Press.

Other volumes in the Representation of Older People in Ageing Research series

Volume 2

INVOLVING OLDER PEOPLE IN RESEARCH
'An amateur doing the work of a professional?'
edited by Sheila Peace

Initiatives have developed throughout the UK that seek to give people 'a greater individual say in how they live their lives and the services they need to help them to do so'. Participation is encouraged at various levels from consultative meetings to users' forums to self-advocacy schemes to direct action.

Gradually, research funders have taken on board the need for researchers to address issues of user participation within their proposed research outlining how these can be met. The three case studies presented in this volume describe ways in which older people have been involved in research as:

* originators of research questions
* advisors on methodology
* fieldworkers
* analysts
* disseminators

Important common points emerge from the studies that will be of value to future discussion over participative research projects involving older people.

Contents: Introduction, *Sheila Peace.* A Meeting of Minds: Older People as Research Advisors, *Elizabeth Mosse and Pat Thornton.* Life on the Margins: Hidden Poverty and the 'Real' Cost of Living for Pensioners, *Dave Goodman and Steve Outram.* Lewisham Older Women's Network: The Health Survey, *Henriette Dodd, Rosalia Mooney, Caroline Williams.* Commentary, *Sheila Peace.* Further Reading.

£8.00   48pp   ISBN 1 901097 25 0   1999

contd.

Volume 3

WRITING OLD AGE
edited by Hannah Zeilig

Can literature provide some universal insight into the ageing process in a way that the social sciences perhaps cannot? In doing biographical research we use terms like 'narrative', 'text' and 'story' - concepts which are used in fiction. As researchers concerned with the study of ageing we seldom draw explicitly on the wealth of imaginative literature which exists about ageing and old age. The papers from this third seminar explore the contribution which the study of literature and creative writing can make to the understanding of old age.

Contents: Introduction, *Brian Gearing and Andrew Blaikie, University of Aberdeen.* Fictions of Age: the Importance of Literature in Understanding Later Life, *Hannah Zeilig, ACIOG.* The Changes and Chances of this Mortal Life: Ageing in the Fiction of Stanley Middleton, *Mike Hepworth, University of Aberdeen.* Finding 'Kate': the Significance of a Poem in Caring, *Joanna Bornat, Open University.* Conclusion, *Andrew Blaikie.*

£10.00   56pp   ISBN 190109755 2   Spring 2000

To order any titles in the series, please make cheque payable to Central Books and send to: Central Books, 99 Wallis Road, London E9 5LN
Telephone: +44(0)20 8986 5488   Fax: +44(0)20 8533 5821
Email: peter@centralbooks.com
Order by fax or phone using a credit card
(Mastercard/VISA/Eurocard/Connect/Delta)
Please add £1.25 for one book and £1.75 for two books.
Orders for three or more books are supplied to customers post free.